ROWAN

The Exmoor Pony

Page 1 Sunrise: Photo by Ruth Chamberlain.

Pages 86 and 87 Sunset: Photo by Nicky Beckett.

First published in Great Britain in 2022

British Library Cataloguing-in-Publication Data
A CIP record for this title is available from the British Library

ISBN 978 0 85704 357 3

Halsgrove
Halsgrove House,
Ryelands Business Park,
Bagley Road, Wellington, Somerset TA21 9PZ
Tel: 01823 653777   Fax: 01823 216796
email: sales@halsgrove.com

Part of the Halsgrove group of companies
Information on all Halsgrove titles is available at: www.halsgrove.com

Printed and bound in India by Parksons Graphics Ltd

ROWAN
The Exmoor Pony

Dawn Westcott

HALSGROVE

 Dawn Westcott is author of best-selling real-life equestrian books, *Wild Pony Whispering*, *Wild Stallion Whispering* and *Wild Herd Whispering* and lives in Exmoor National Park with her farmer husband Nick and a large herd of Exmoor ponies, 'Holtball' Herd 11. Together, they founded the Exmoor Pony Project to help safeguard, promote and improve welfare for one of the British Isles most ancient, and endangered, native pony breeds. Dawn has trained her wild-born Exmoor stallion Bear to stand supreme champion of the Exmoor breed and win two world championships in horse agility. She encourages taming, handling and training Exmoor ponies with kindness, patience and empathy, to build trust. These sentiments are expressed in the story of *Rowan The Exmoor Pony*.

Find out more

Find out more about the Exmoor Pony Project and Dawn Westcott at www.wildponywhispering.co.uk.

Front Cover: *Thank you to the brilliant equestrian artist, Rebecca de Mendonca*

Thank you to

Nick Westcott, Heather Williams, Millie Ker, Geoff Baylis, Rex Milton, Jane Pearn, Christina Williams, Mel and Paul McGee, Susannah and Ya'Acov Darling Khan, Mike Mellor, Peter Hotchkiss, Richard Broad, Sue Butterfield and Exmoor National Park Authority.

Photographs and research for artworks: Geoff Baylis, Nicky Beckett, Martin Buschmann, Ruth Chamberlain, Sarah Hailstone, Paris Catarina Cataldo, Rachel Davies, T.Gibson, Jessica Please, Murray Sanders, Jamie and Lisa Waters, A.Vowels, Dawn Westcott.

Dedication

This book is dedicated to my wonderful husband
Nick Westcott, my mother Heather Williams,
our friend Millie Ker and our herd of
Exmoor ponies – and to Her Majesty,
Queen Elizabeth II, for the Platinum Jubilee.

Contents

Life On Exmoor

Fresh breeze on my face
as I draw in the air,
my velvety muzzle
close to her hair.

My mother is gentle,
loving and kind.
Enchantingly pretty
and fast as a hind.

We move like the wind,
if there's cause for alarm.
Staying close to her side,
she protects me from harm.

Our home is on Exmoor,
we live wild and free.
We go where we like –
there's so much to see.

Emerald grasses,
bushes and trees.
Rivers and streams
roll away to the seas.

When I am tired
I lay down to sleep.
Flat on my side,
until up I must leap.

With ponies all round me
the herd is my life.
Siblings to play with,
no trouble or strife.

My father the stallion
is handsome and bold.
His powerful strength
is a sight to behold.

When we feel brave
we approach him to play,
and if he's inclined,
he'll show us the way.

We copy his moves,
rearing up to each other.
Snorting and prancing,
sisters and brothers.

Robin my brother
is my special friend.
Days spent together
from beginning to end.

The luminous moon,
the red setting sun,
the sparkling stars.
So much love, so much fun.

The Pony Gathering

As autumn approaches
the trees turn to gold.
Our coats become thicker,
we don't feel the cold.

The herd becomes restless.
There's noise over yonder.
Horses and bikes,
what is it we wonder?

Wind whips around us,
we're galloping now,
from the moor to the farm,
sweat drips from our brows.

Clattering hooves,
we're shut in the pen.
Swirling and twirling,
surrounded by men.

Wild eyed and frisky,
my mother is tense.
I stay close by her side –
we can't jump the fence.

I'm moved from the pen –
I let out a cry.
My mother is watching,
we know it's goodbye.

There's no time to look
as we're taken away.
The foals to a barn,
how long will we stay?

Where is the moor?
The breeze on my face?
Where is my mother?
What is this dark place?

A New Home

Foals all together,
huddled and wary.
Nibbling the hay,
this new life is scary.

Some people arrive
and come in to see.
It's clear to us foals,
they're looking at me.

"His name is Rowan,
a very good sort.
He's strong and well-moving."
I let out a snort.

Soon there is noise,
we're moving around.
In front is a ramp
and I'm up in a bound.

Shut in the trailer,
my whinnying cry.
My heart's in my mouth,
as my siblings reply.

Robin is loudest.
I want to get out.
Can't he come with me?
"Don't part us!" I shout.

Everything moves,
I struggle to stand.
We're leaving the farm,
I don't understand.

We finally stop,
I leap down the ramp.
Fresh straw awaits me,
my coat is all damp.

I'm back in a barn
and there in the light,
are calm pony faces –
I might be all right.

"Hello young foal,"
they're saying to me.
"You're in a good place,
as kind as can be."

I reach up to sniff
each muzzle in turn.
The warmth of their breath,
but still my heart yearns.

My legs are unsteady,
I start to sink down.
My eyelids are heavy,
I sleep with a frown.

Learning To Trust

My nose in the corner,
someone comes near.
"Don't try to touch me!"
"You've nothing to fear."

My rumbling tummy
is keen for their food.
Shall I just take it?
I don't want to be rude.

Snatching a mouthful,
I'm not sure I should.
Yet crunching and chewing,
these pellets taste good.

The voices are strange,
I freeze in alarm.
They're trying to tell me,
"We mean you no harm."

Give me the time,
you have to, you must.
For this is the way,
you will win my trust.

Joining The Herd

I'm alone in this stable.
What can I do?
The others have gone,
I'd like to go too.

They answer my wish,
the door opens wide.
I stare for a moment,
then venture outside.

The people are there,
they show me the way.
The path to the field,
where the herd is at play.

I canter towards them,
then stand for the greeting.
Licking and chewing,
with respect for the meeting.

Soon I'm amongst them,
I'm now in the herd!
My young heart is singing
as loud as a bird.

I stay close to Harry,
he looks just like me.
Yet older and bigger,
a safe place to be.

Connecting

Holding a bowl,
they invite me to come.
I pause, then approach,
keen to take some.

My heart skips a beat,
as I reach for the food.
They stand there quite still,
trying not to intrude.

Stretching my neck,
I sniff at their hand.
A great leap of faith,
the closer I stand.

They're moving the bowl
and I leap right away.
Trembling and snorting,
small steps every day.

Slowly and surely,
my confidence grows.
Now I eat from the bowl
and sniff at their toes.

A hand extends forwards,
gentle and slow.
My muzzle makes contact,
our energies flow.

My heart takes a leap,
two creatures connect.
Two friends in the making,
a mutual respect.

Letting them stroke me,
I quite like the touch.
It's soothing and calming,
I've missed that so much.

Today is a good day.
I'm starting to feel,
my new life is bright.
I'm beginning to heal.

I've friends in the pasture
to play with all day.
They call us at twilight,
we all know the way.

Head Collars and Ropes

Sometimes the ponies
are led by a rope,
away from the herd.
Returning, I hope.

Back in the field,
they talk of adventure.
Riding and jumping,
they need a thirst quencher.

Excited and happy
they get down to roll.
Muddy and sweaty,
from tail up to poll.

It's my turn to wear
the head collar now.
Soon it is on,
I'm not quite sure how.

Slipped off my head,
soon after it's on,
they seem really pleased
– and I'm glad it's gone.

Soon I am able
to walk with the rope.
Joining the others,
for adventures I hope.

Summer

Summer time brings
a move to new pasture.
A valley with woods,
to trot and go faster.

Sometimes wild stags
arrive for a visit.
Massive great horns,
they're truly exquisite.

Foxes and rabbits,
dash into their holes.
We also see badgers
and small water voles.

As winter approaches,
we're back at the farm.
There's shelter and hay,
we'll come to no harm.

Agility Play

I continue to grow –
by spring I am strong.
Keen to explore
and play all day long.

I'm starting to learn
to push a large ball,
walk on tarpaulin,
through spaces so small.

Jump little obstacles,
stop when they ask,
navigate backwards
and walk round a cask.

"This is agility."
I hear them say.
It helps to prepare us
for riding one day.

A Foal Arrives

It's autumn again
and winter is near.
A new foal arrives,
Her eyes full of fear.

My muzzle is first,
I respond to her call.
The foal reaches up,
so frightened and small.

It's my turn to tell her,
"This place is all right.
We're here to look out
as you sleep in the night."

She comes in the field –
we're feeling aloof!
Show us good manners,
or we'll show a hoof.

She follows me close.
I remember those days.
When I pined for my herd
and our free-living ways.

Soon we are playful.
"Go faster I dare!"
The wind on our faces,
we haven't a care.

The Farrier

The farrier's here,
he's trimming my feet.
I'm quiet and patient,
they look very neat.

My hooves are hard wearing,
so no metal shoes.
I've very hard soles,
which don't seem to bruise.

Living and galloping,
out on the moor,
has given us feet
that our people adore.

Hairy Exmoors

Exmoors are hardy,
resilient, robust.
Nature's designed us
to not need much fuss.

Used to the cold,
we've thick winter coats.
No clipping or rugging
– perhaps a few oats!

When springtime arrives,
our coats start to shed.
We love a good brush,
from our tail to our head.

The birds line their nests
with buckets of hair.
It comes out in handfuls,
and gets everywhere.

Preparing for Showing

Our coats become sleek
as summer arrives.
Ready for shows,
to which we will drive.

There is the trailer,
my heart skips a beat.
I remember that trip,
so unsure on my feet.

This time they ask me
to walk in and out.
Pausing for carrots,
so I haven't a doubt.

My confidence grows
and we go for a ride.
I'm still feeling wary,
but calmer inside.

My First Show

Preparing for showing,
we do lots of walking.
Harry beside me,
as they're busy talking.

We're groomed to a shine,
our hooves painted black.
In the trailer we go,
with lots of clean tack.

The ramp clatters down,
and out we are led.
A lot going on
and show rings ahead.

It's really quite clear
That I need to behave.
Show off my paces,
for a smile and a wave.

Someone beside us
gives a pony a smack.
I jolt with the shock,
as the whip makes a crack.

A hand strokes my shoulder,
thank goodness they're kind.
If it happened to me,
I'd certainly mind.

Walking in circles,
they ask me to trot.
I spring into action,
give it all that I've got.

We stand in the line up,
everyone's still.
The judge points at me,
I've won – what a thrill!

A rather big ribbon
is pinned to my bridle.
The breeze makes it flap,
and sideways I sidle.

We're off round the ring,
with a trot and a leap.
A big lap of honour
and rosettes to keep.

When we are home,
from the trailer I glide.
Dancing about,
and bursting with pride.

Back in the field,
heads lift from grazing.
I don't like to boast,
but I'm truly amazing!

Learning To Ride

Four years of age,
the saddle is ready,
to sit on my back,
if I keep nice and steady.

As I'm still young,
they sit on me lightly.
Short little rides,
asking politely.

Suddenly a pheasant,
bursts up from the ground.
I leap in the air
and spin right around.

Sadly my rider,
slips off my back.
Hits the ground with a thud,
letting go of my tack.

I watch her get up,
lowering my head.
Feeling relieved,
she's alive and not dead.

No one is angry,
so I don't run away.
Together we're learning,
to find the right way.

Soon we are cantering,
smiles on our faces.
Adventures ahead,
in wide open spaces.

I try not to stumble,
or put in a buck.
I look after my rider,
so we don't come unstuck.

Agility's taught me,
when I face a puzzle,
to not bolt away –
explore with my muzzle.

My rider allows me
the time to digest,
these curious things
in front of my chest.

Sometimes I'm ridden
around in the school.
In straight lines and circles,
learning the rules.

A touch to my side,
a squeeze from the seat.
Hands gently guide me,
I'm coming on a treat.

Jumping

Today we are jumping
some colourful poles.
To not knock them down
is one of our goals.

Lead Rein

Now I am older
and no longer wild,
they feel I am ready
to carry a child.

Small hands on my nose,
they're rushing about.
I try not to spook
as they let out a shout.

A lead rope is held,
they're checking my tack.
A cute little person,
is set on my back.

We're walking in circles,
a slow steady pace.
I'm very aware,
that this isn't a race.

We break into trot,
I'm doing my best.
A shriek of delight
says I'm passing the test.

I practice with children
time and again,
until we are ready
to show in Lead Rein.

We're at a big show,
the judging is soon.
Then over the ring,
floats a hot air balloon!

Ponies are leaping,
the handlers fumble.
It's not unsurprising,
that some riders tumble.

I had a spook,
but I'm coming back.
The reason is clear –
I won't get a smack.

The trust that was given,
when I was a colt,
means when there's a shock,
I remember to halt.

"You're a very good pony."
The judge strokes my nose,
as I stand for the ribbons,
and make a nice pose.

Dressage

This week it's Dressage,
we've practised the test.
I think I'll remember –
we'll make up the rest...

We're both very smart,
my rider and I.
My brown coat is gleaming,
I hold my head high.

We trot down the centre,
the judge sitting there.
Who's that in the mirror?
I stand there and stare.

How very unyielding
a pony can be,
when looking at someone,
exactly like me.

Then we go forwards,
a little too fast.
We miss a few turnings
– I'm having a blast.

The mark sheets are up,
we're bottom today.
The comments imply
that I get my own way.

First place or last place,
my people are grinning.
They love us to bits,
it's not just about winning.

Cross Country

We're going cross country,
the wind in our faces.
Ahead are the jumps
in challenging places.

Legs squeeze my sides,
hands offer the reins.
Over we zoom,
on this tricky terrain.

We're galloping now,
the finish in sight.
We're over the jumps,
we've done it all right.

People are clapping.
"The Exmoor is clear!"
We're crossing the line,
I'm hearing them cheer.

A hand on my shoulder,
arms round my neck.
A face in my mane,
a stroke and a peck.

We're on our way home,
I'm eating my hay.
Soon back in the field
to report on the day.

A Herd Snooze

The sun rises slowly,
grass covered in dew.
A new day awakens,
the sky glimmers blue.

One after another,
we lie down to snooze.
The sun on our backs,
we'll do what we choose.

Snoring and dreaming,
the herd is asleep.
With some of us
watching,
if up we must leap.

A Break In

Exmoors are nosy,
we like to explore.
Especially if
there's a half open door.

A nudge then a push
and we're in with the feeds.
"Let's tip these over,
look here – nuts and seeds!"

It doesn't take long,
to create such a mess.
Soon they come running
in a state of distress.

"What did they eat?"
"Oh no! Call the vet!"
Don't worry dear humans,
we're not ill just yet.

I'm put in the stable
to see if I bloat.
For close observation,
I can't help but gloat.

I managed to eat
half a sack of the feed.
My tummy is gurgling
because of my greed.

A new lock is fastened
on the feed store.
It may take some time
to get in for more.

A Great Escape

One day we spotted
the gate was left open.
We went down the track –
the fence there was broken.

A lovely big garden
with plenty of fruit.
Luscious green grass,
what a joy, what a hoot.

Suddenly shrieking
fills up the air.
"My garden, my lawn!
There they are, over there!"

Snatching a mouthful,
we bolt to the fence.
Jumping like stags,
it makes so much sense.

The lane is a long one,
it leads to the road.
We know this from riding,
we know where it goes.

Fresh breeze on my face,
I remember those days,
of galloping free
in our wild pony ways.

Yet the hedges are juicy,
there's so much to eat.
This outing's a fun one,
these berries are sweet.

There's just enough time,
to say Hi to the donkey.
We hear him sometimes,
his ears are all wonky.

Our people arrive,
they're still getting dressed.
There's no need to worry,
they seem really stressed.

We soon return home
and they visit the garden.
Taking some gifts
and seeking a pardon.

The County Show

This show is special,
we're here for our breed.
To find the best Exmoor,
a truly fine steed.

The stallion is awesome,
his paces so good.
Here for the Championship,
that's understood.

I'll try very hard,
I might win a place.
There's stiff competition,
I'm in for the race.

There in the ring,
a meeting of eyes.
It's my brother Robin!
A lovely surprise.

I let out a whinny,
he calls out my name.
I want to be near him,
and he feels the same.

The stallion is giving
his very best trot.
Then something spooks him,
he's off like a shot.

Out of the ring,
everyone's shouting.
His handler is chasing,
the judges are pouting.

The judging continues –
we're in the parade.
I've won Champion Exmoor!
I've made the grade.

The showing is finished,
we're on our way home.
I think about Robin
and feel all alone.

Everyone greets me,
I know I'm a star.
But inside I'm hoping
that Robin's not far.

He reminds me of when
on the moor we would roam.
Galloping, playing,
the place we called home.

A Broken Heart

Life at the farm
Is the best you can find.
But brothers are special,
they're one of a kind.

Back in the field,
I can't shake my mood.
My coat becomes listless,
I've gone off my food.

After a while,
The vet takes a look.
But can't find a cause,
in the veterinary book.

I've lost my sparkle,
as sad as can be.
I yearn for my brother,
to live here with me.

They stroke me a lot,
we go out for walks.
"What's made you so sad?
I wish you could talk?"

"Did you see at the show,
that pony he met?
Is it possible that,
Rowan's filled with regret?"

They make some enquiries
and find we're related.
Robin's for sale
and they are elated.

They're seeking a pony,
an Exmoor like me.
For riding in pairs –
how smart we would be.

My Brother and Me

A lorry arrives.
Is that Robin I see?
I cannot believe it,
walking over to me.

Whinnies and whickers,
we're so keen to greet.
I'm tossing my head,
banging rails with my feet.

Our people are laughing,
and open the gate.
Robin is home now,
it's never too late.

The wind on our faces,
we gallop together.
We'll never be parted,
not now or ever.

Life at the farm,
is the best it can be.
The herd and our people,
and Robin with me.

The End

Author's Note

"Ponies are sentient beings with emotions and feelings. They have their own language and yet, when we take the time to be still and connect with them, it's amazing how much we can mutually understand. Giving us a precious opportunity to learn from, respect and trust each other. Please remember to be kind and patient with ponies (and all animals) and you will be a better person for it."

Dawn Westcott

Dawn Westcott's Books

WILD PONY WHISPERING

Wild Pony Whispering is the captivating real-life story of starving orphaned wild-born Exmoor foal, Monsieur Chapeau, and how he flourished and showed us how to better understand and tame the wild ponies of Exmoor. Richly illustrated with colour photographs, this book offers valuable insights into equine behaviour, socialising and training ponies, along with highlighting the challenges facing this charismatic endangered native pony breed.

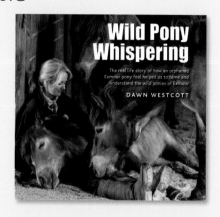

ISBN 978 0 85704 276 7 (Published in hardback by Halsgrove Publishing £14.99)

WILD STALLION WHISPERING

Wild Stallion Whispering is the real-life story of wild-born Exmoor colt, Bear, who found himself unwanted after leaving the moor – and his incredible journey to becoming twice world champion in international horse agility and standing supreme champion of the Exmoor breed. His story follows the roller-coaster of highs and lows and disasters and triumphs that have shaped the life of this magnificent stallion.

ISBN 978 0 85704 293 4 (Published in hardback by Halsgrove Publishing £14.99)

WILD HERD WHISPERING

Wild Herd Whispering is a series of enchanting, inter-woven, real-life stories, starting with a tiny five-week-old moorbred Exmoor filly who faces the bleakest future. This book explores the amazing and enlightening world of herd dynamics and energy, offering invaluable insights into how ponies think and learn – and what they want. Readers can also catch up with the ongoing adventures of Monsieur Chapeau, his chums and Bear the stallion.

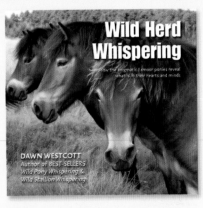

ISBN 978 0 85704 318 4 (Published in hardback by Halsgrove Publishing £14.99)

Below: Herd 23 Exmoor ponies on Withypool Common. Photo: Geoff Baylis.

The Exmoor Pony Project

Nick and Dawn Westcott married in 2008 and re-established the Westcott family's ancient Herd 11 with the 'Holtball' prefix, and their supreme champion pedigree Exmoor stallion Bear and his mare Maisie.

Nick's family has lived and farmed in the Exmoor parishes for over 500 years, with Exmoor ponies continuing a family tradition dating back (in written records) to 1872.

Nick's great, great grandfather, Robert Westcott, great grandfather, Arthur George Westcott and grandfather, Cyril Westcott, are pictured(opposite page) on the annual Exmoor pony drive from Porlock to Bampton Pony Sale in 1920. Nick was born at Buckethole Farm, Stoke Pero, Porlock, before moving to Woodcocks Ley Farm, Luccombe, in 1973 and taking over Holt Ball Farm, Luccombe, in 1985, where he lives with Dawn.

Nick and Dawn founded the Exmoor Pony Project in 2013 to help safeguard and promote endangered Exmoor ponies and they work with other Exmoor herd owners to promote and find good opportunities for semi-feral foals coming off the moor. They maintain a large herd of Exmoor ponies on the farm, which produces the popular 'Exmoor Pony Poop Compost'.

"Nick has generously helped save and safeguard Exmoor ponies from a range of moorland herds, including some orphans, and has stood up to obstructions and challenges to their welfare and

Left: Nick Westcott (right) with Jimmer Milton at the Herd 23 gathering from Withypool Common in 2021.

survival with a strength and dignity that would make his ancestors proud. The animals are drawn to his kind, assured nature, which in itself brings a deep connection with Nature," said Dawn.

The Exmoor Pony Project encourages better understanding, handling and treatment of Exmoor ponies and campaigns for welfare and management improvements. Nick and Dawn are also co-founders of the Moorland Exmoor Pony Breeders Group (MEPBG), comprising Exmoor herd owners and land owners working together to safeguard endangered Exmoor ponies. This work includes being part of the Exmoor Pony Genome Project (genotyping and sequencing the whole genome of the Exmoor pony) and working with the Equus Survival Trust in the US to facilitate DNA profiling and authenticated lineage tracking to help safeguard the important population of purebred Exmoor ponies excluded from the closed Exmoor pony stud book.

"The Exmoor Pony Project can be accredited with giving us and the public a much better representation and understanding of true moorland bred Exmoor ponies, widening the audience massively – and sales are reflecting this."

Rex Milton, Exmoor farmer and owner of 'Withypoole' Herd 23, the oldest family-owned herd of Exmoor ponies, running on Anstey and Withypool Commons.

Find out more about the Exmoor Pony Project at
www.WildPonyWhispering.co.uk

The Exmoor Pony Breed

Exmoor ponies are one of the most ancient British native pony breeds and they are endangered. The ponies have grazed the moors of Exmoor for hundreds (if not thousands) of years and are truly integral to the cultural landscape. There are only about 500 ponies in Exmoor National Park and around 3000 worldwide.

Intelligent, tough, resilient and charismatic, Exmoor ponies have evolved to survive and thrive on tough moorland, with its challenging terrain and weather conditions. Living and breeding in this environment, the semi-feral ponies retain the learned and genetic characteristics and behaviours of extensively-grazing free living animals – and their 'wildness factor'.

In Exmoor National Park, the semi-feral Exmoor pony herds run wild and free all year round in different moorland areas, including the uplands of Brendon Common, Buscombe, the Dunkery Commons, Withypool Common, Anstey

Common, Molland Moor, Porlock Hill, Haddon Hill, North Hill, Winsford Hill and the cliffs at Countisbury and Foreland. The ponies are all owned by someone and there are around twenty moorland herds. Sometimes, a stallion runs with the mares and sometimes mares are brought in ground to the farms to be covered by a stallion, before returning to the moor to foal. Some are kept in ground on the farms. Breeding stallions must be inspected for quality  and licensed to ensure that foals can be registered as pedigree Exmoor ponies.

Each autumn, the herd owners gather (round up) their ponies into handling pens, to check them over and wean the foals. Foals are then inspected, microchipped and registered in the Exmoor pony stud book – as long as the DNA samples taken from their manes are able to prove their sire and dam. Some foals return to their herds and others are sold to different herds or new homes. Colt foals must come off the moor to ensure that only pedigree Exmoor stallions are used for breeding.

With kind, patient handling and socialisation, Exmoor ponies can learn to trust people and become excellent riding, driving and performance ponies, ridden by small adults as well as children. With their moorland heritage, they also have the perfect qualities for conservation and rewilding grazing schemes.

Left: Tippbarlake Herd Exmoor ponies on Brendon Common. Photo: Geoff Baylis.

Exmoor Pony Characteristics

Exmoor ponies are strongly built with a robust digestive system that helps them thrive on rough, moorland grazing and vegetation. They range in colour from golden brown to reddish bay and dark brown. They have dark manes and tails, sometimes with blond or flame-coloured flashes.

Exmoor ponies have distinct pale 'mealy' markings around their eyes, muzzle and under belly – and their 'toad' eyes have a padded layer to help dispel rain. They grow thick, double-layered winter coats which provide highly effective insulation, and a fan of short hairs (shute) at the top of their tails. Their lower legs are black, with hard black hooves.

Their intelligent pony characters make them feisty, resourceful and questioning. They are incredibly intuitive and in tune with nature – for example, they are experts at sensing incoming stormy weather and moving rapidly to the best available shelter. These skills are also put to good use when reading humans – making Exmoor ponies some of the best equine teachers in the world for people who want to better understand equine behaviour.

Left and on page 78: Exmoor ponies from the Farleywater Herd on Buscombe. Photo: Sarah Hailstone.

Exmoor National Park

Exmoor National Park is an area of beautiful, hilly open moorland stretching across West Somerset into North Devon in South West England, which was designated a National Park in 1954. It is named after the River Exe (which starts 2 miles north-west of Simonsbath). There are 692.8 km² (267.5 square miles) of spectacular terrain and breathtaking natural beauty – including moorland, steep combes, forests, river valleys, pretty villages, farmland, cliffs and 55 km (34 miles) of the Bristol Channel coast. The largest settlements are Porlock, Dulverton, Lynton and Lynmouth.

Visitors can see the semi-feral Exmoor pony herds grazing in their moorland areas across Exmoor. The National Park is also home to the magnificent wild red deer and many other kinds of wildlife, including otters, beavers and rare butterflies, bats and birds – as well as cattle and sheep, including the famous Exmoor Horn sheep and Red Devon cattle. The Exmoor National Park Authority was established in 1997 with two main purposes;

1. To conserve and enhance the natural beauty, wildlife and cultural heritage of the National Park.
2. To promote opportunities for the understanding and enjoyment of the special qualities of the National Park by the public.

Find out more about Exmoor National Park at
www.Exmoor-NationalPark.gov.uk.

The Rowan Tree
('Wizard Tree')

The Rowan is a beautiful tree with a mystical history which enjoys growing in high altitude, upland areas like Exmoor. Its leaves and berries are loved by wildlife and the berries make excellent jam. Rowan produces dense clusters of creamy-white flowers which, following pollination by insects, develop into scarlet fruits. The seeds are then dispersed by birds. Its Celtic name is *fid na ndruad* which means 'Wizard's tree' and it was once planted near dwellings and in churchyards as protection against witches and spirits. The Rowan's bright red fruits are thought to represent the best colour for fighting evil. The wood was used to stir milk and prevent it curdling and to make divining rods and pocket charms.

Source information: www.woodlandtrust.org.uk

The Rowan tree on Withypool Common, home of the Herd 23 Exmoor ponies. Photo: Nicky Beckett.

Rebecca de Mendonca
Equestrian Artist

> 'The energy of these beautiful ponies, their connection with the moor and also with each other, is truly inspiring.'

Rebecca is an artist based near Exeter, in the South West of England, inspired by horses and people and the dramatic landscape around her. She paints to capture a moment in time, and what it feels like to be there, breathing life and energy into her subjects. Rebecca is an associate member of the Society of Equestrian Artists

and her work has become widely known for its energy, life and movement. She paints horses, people, landscapes and architecture, always seeking out the atmosphere and emotion in her subjects.

A long-standing and generous supporter of the Exmoor Pony Project, Rebecca has produced a number of beautiful pastels of Exmoor ponies, including the cover of *Rowan The Exmoor Pony*.

Find out more at www.rebeccademendonca.co.uk

Monsieur Chapeau of Wild Pony Whispering.

Pictured, above: Painting of Holtball Herd 11's Supreme Breed Champion stallion, Hawkwell Versuvius 'Bear', mare Maisie and foal, Holtball Kilimanjaro.
Right: Gelding, D'Artagnan.

Glossary

Agility – an equestrian activity where ponies navigate obstacles and challenges, on a lead rope or loose (at liberty).

Arena (or manege) – a soft-surface area to train and school ponies.

Barn – a large farm building used for storing grain, hay and straw and housing livestock.

Bloat – an accumulation of gas in the stomach (over eating).

Bolt – an alarmed horse galloping off at high speed when their 'fight or flight' response is triggered.

Breed – a stock of animals within a species having a distinctive appearance and typically having been developed by deliberate selection. Exmoor ponies are a 'breed' of British native pony.

Bridle – the head gear used on a pony to which the reins are attached, for riding or leading.

Buck – when the pony plants the front feet on the ground and throws its hind end upward.

Canter – the pace of a pony between trot and gallop, with not less than one foot on the ground at any time.

Cask – a large container like a barrel used for carrying liquids. Sometimes referred to as a 'drum'. Empty casks are ideal for pony agility.

Centre Line – riding down the centre of the Dressage arena.

Chest – the front of a pony, measured from the bottom of the neck to the top of the front legs.

Clipping – shaving off a horse's thick winter coat to reduce sweating during riding. Clipped ponies then need to wear a rug to protect them from cold and wet.

Coat – A pony's coat is known as 'hair'. Exmoor ponies grow a thick double-layered winter coat, comprising a soft 'down' undercoat and a longer, coarse outer coat, which protects them from bad weather. In summer, they shed this thick coat and grow a sleek, shiny summer coat.

Colt – a young uncastrated male, who is under four years old. Once castrated (testicles are removed by a veterinary surgeon) the male becomes a gelding. If not castrated, the colt matures into a stallion.

Connection – being fully aware of your 'here right now' experience, fully in touch with what is happening in the present moment. The relationship between a person and pony, where each is able to acknowledge the other – to connect.

County Show – a summer agricultural show where farmers, breeders and owners show off their animals and judges award prizes to the best exhibits. There are also trade stands, activities and entertainment.

Cross Country – an equestrian activity to prove the speed, endurance and jumping ability of an equine going 'across country', that forms one of the three phases of the sport of Eventing (Dressage, Cross Country and Show Jumping).

Dressage – an equestrian activity with the aim of evolving ridden obedience, flexibility, and balance. Ridden tests are carried out in an indoor or outdoor arena. Dressage is also one of the three phases of the sport of Eventing (Dressage, Cross Country and Show Jumping).

Elated – very happy.

Enchanting – captivating; delightfully attractive.

Equine or Equus – a genus of mammals in the family Equidae, which includes horses, ponies, donkeys, mules and zebras.

Exmoor National Park – a beautiful national park in the South West of England, spanning West Somerset and North Devon and comprising 692 km^2 of moorland wilderness, dramatic coastline, farmed land and villages. Home to Exmoor ponies, moorland cattle and sheep, wild red deer and other wildlife.

Exmoor Pony – one of the British Isles most ancient native pony breeds.

Exquisite – extremely beautiful.

Farm – an area of land and buildings used for growing crops and rearing animals.

Farrier – someone who shoes equines with metal shoes or who trims and rasps the feet of unshod equines.

Foal – a young pony up to one year old, at which time they become a 'yearling'.

Forelock – the hair growing out of the top of horse's head which flows down over the forehead.

Frisky – full of energy; playful.

Gallop – the fastest pace of a horse or pony with all the feet off the ground in each stride.

Gelding – a castrated male pony. Once castrated (testicles are removed by a veterinary surgeon) the gelding cannot breed.

Gloat – dwelling on their own success, or another's misfortune, with smugness or pleasure.

Good Sort – a person of a kindly and likeable disposition. A nice person (or pony).

Grazing – pasture suitable for animals, like horses and ponies, who get their food from eating grass. Also describes the activity of eating grass.

Grooming – the cleaning, brushing and care given to a pony to enhance their physical appearance.

Horse hair – hair from a pony's mane or tail, or the hair in their coats.

Halt – asking a pony to stand still, and the action of standing still. Asking for a halt contradicts their natural instinct to move away. A pony that chooses to calmly halt rather than run away is showing trust.

Halter – Thin rope head gear that fits around the pony's head to which a lead rope can be attached.

Handler – a person who trains or who has charge of a pony from the ground.

Hardy – capable of enduring difficult conditions.

Harry – 'Uncle Harry' is a mature Exmoor pony gelding who is a wonderful 'Uncle' to foals and youngsters, helping to reassure and guide them.

Hay – grass that has been mown (cut) and then dried and baled for use as forage (food) for ponies.

Head Collar – head gear that fits around the pony's head, fastening with buckles, to which a lead rope can be attached to lead or tie up a pony.

Herd – a group of ponies that live together.

Hind – a female deer, especially a red deer. Red deer live wild in Exmoor National Park.

Horse Show – an event involving competitions and displays in various equestrian sports such as Showing, Show Jumping and Dressage. Small local events or large national events. Sometimes with trade stands.

Hoof or hooves – the horny part of a pony's feet.

Horns – on Exmoor, stags' antlers are referred to as 'horns'.

Hot Air Balloon – a large balloon filled with heated air which floats in the sky with a basket underneath for people to ride in.

Huddle – crowded together, nestling closely.

Judges – equestrian experts who evaluate the conformation of equines for a suitable purpose, or the ability of a horse to perform certain requirements for a class. They then decide where to place the competitors and award rosettes, prizes and sometimes qualifying cards for higher level competitions, to the winners.

Jumping – riding ponies over a set course of obstacles. In competitions, the winner is judged according to ability and speed. Jumps may be set up in an arena (show jumping) or created with more natural, wilder materials (cross country). In agility, ponies jump obstacles either ridden, or with the handler running alongside holding a rope, or completely loose (at liberty).

Lap of Honour – the winner of a horse showing class or championship making a circuit of the show ring with their horse or pony.

Lead Rein – a Lead Rein pony is ridden by a small child and led by an an adult.

Lead Rope – a long lead line (rope or strap) which is attached to a head collar, halter or bridle, used to lead a horse.

Line Up – where the competitors in a horse showing class are called in by the Judge (or steward) to be assessed or to award placings and decide a winner.

Luminous – the way the brilliant light of the moon is perceived by the eye.

Mane – the long, coarse hair growing in a line from the horse's head – from the forelock to the base of neck. It can fall to one side of the neck or the other, and sometimes splits, falling down both sides of the neck.

Mare – a female adult horse, four years of age and over.

Mark Sheet (Dressage) – the sheet on which a Dressage Judge makes comments and awards marks to give an overall score and placing in the competition.

Metal Shoes – 'U' shaped metal plates (shoes) that are nailed to the bottom of horses hooves to protect them from hard or rough surfaces. Exmoor ponies have evolved very tough feet from living on the moors and can often be ridden 'barefoot' without the need for metal shoes.

Mirror (Dressage) – a mirror in an indoor dressage arena enables riders to watch their horses while they are riding. Or indeed, for ponies to look at themselves!

Moor – an area of open uncultivated upland, typically covered with heather.

Muzzle – the protruding area of a horse's face including the nose and mouth. Exmoor ponies have 'mealy muzzles' which are light beige in colour.

Native Pony – particular breeds of ponies native to the British Isles, evolved by deliberate selection. Often of ancient origin.

Nibble – taking small bites. For example, eating hay.

Oats – a grain fed to horses and ponies that is easily digested raw.

Paces – describes the speed of a horse when walking or moving faster. The four paces (or gaits) of a horse are walk, trot, canter and gallop.

Parade – at big horse shows, the winners and/or Champions of the various breed and competitive sections will take part in a parade and the show judges will choose a Supreme Champion of Show and Reserve Supreme Champion. This may include a qualifier for the overall winner to compete in a national championship, such as at the Horse of the Year Show.

Pasture – land covered with grass and plants suitable for grazing animals such as horses and ponies, sheep and cattle.

Peck – a quick and casual kiss.

Pellets – small, rounded, compressed mass of horse feed containing various cereals, minerals and nutrients, i.e. a scoop of pellets.

Pens – refers to handling pens for containing and inspecting livestock. These can be made of metal, interlocking stock pen panels, or from wood or plastic.

Pheasant – a large long-tailed game bird native to Asia, the male of which typically has bright colouring (plumage, feathers).

Placing (in a show) – the order in which the horse show judge puts competitors, usually awarding rosettes from 1st to 6th place.

Poles – the brightly coloured wooden or plastic poles used for show jumping, or sometimes plain wooden poles used in cross country and working hunter jumping classes.

Poll – the area of the horse's head immediately between and behind the ears.

Pony Nuts – also referred to as pellets. Small, rounded compressed mass of horse feed, containing various cereals, minerals and nutrients, i.e. a scoop of pony nuts.

Pony – a horse of small breed, especially below 14 hands 2 inches (147.32cm, measured from the wither to the ground).

Pony Gathering – the annual event where semi-feral, free-living pony herds are rounded up from their moorland areas and drifted either to pens situated on the moorland, or to the farms belonging to the herd owners. Here the foals are weaned from their mothers and inspected and given passports. Some may return to the moor and others must be found new homes elsewhere.

Pose – getting into a particular position to be photographed or otherwise admired.

Pout – pushing the lips forward as an expression of annoyance.

Prance – the movement of a horse with high, springy steps.

Rails – lengths of square or rounded wood which are fastened (nailed or screwed) to posts to make a fence.

Ramp – the back of a horse trailer that lowers to the ground allowing the horse to walk up and enter the trailer.

Rear – when a horse stands up on their hind legs with the forelegs off the ground. This dramatic movement can be linked to fear, aggression, dominance, posturing or playfulness.

Resilient – able to withstand or recover quickly from difficult conditions.

Reins – long narrow straps attached to each side of a horse's bit (the metal bar the horse wears in their mouth from which the rider can steer) or to each side of the bridle (if there is no bit) which the rider holds in their hands to steer and communicate with the horse.

Ribbons – another term for 'rosette'. Technically, the ribbons are the long flowing 'tails' attached to the actual rosette. Awarded as prizes for achieving a place in a horse showing class or other equestrian competition.

Ride (and riding) – the activity of riding a horse. To sit on their back and control their movement.

Robust – strong and healthy.

Roll – when a horse lies down and rolls from side to side. They like to roll on grass, dirt and bedding to help shed moulting hair, or when they're sweaty or itchy. Sometimes, they cover themselves in dust, mud or sand as a barrier against cold and/or flies and midges. They will often roll after lying down to sleep or after exercise.

Rope – a length of strong cord made by twisting together materials like hemp, sisal or nylon, etc. A rope is used to lead a horse.

Rosette – a rose-shaped decoration, made with ribbon, with ribbon tails, which is awarded as a price to winners in an equestrian competition.

Rowan – a small deciduous tree of the rose family which grows wild in Exmoor National Park.

Rugging – putting a rug (coat) on a horse to protect them from flies, rain or cold weather.

Saddle – a seat fastened on the back of a horse for riding.

Sash – a long strip of satin-like material which drapes around the neck of Championship winners at horse shows and competitions. Awarded with rosettes and sometimes a trophy.

School (as in arena) – an enclosed area, usually with a soft surface like sand or sand/fibre or sand/rubber, where horses are trained. These can be inside or outside.

Seat – the way the rider positions their body while sitting on a horse.

Shed – as in shedding hair. Ponies shed both their winter and summer coats, while the new coat grows through.

Showing – taking horses and ponies to a show to exhibit them in a show ring in front of a judge, where they can be assessed and the best (in the opinion of that judge) are chosen as winners.

Showing Preparation – getting ponies ready for a show includes practising for the show, then washing and grooming the ponies and cleaning tack and clothes, so everything is ready for the competition.

Show Ring – the enclosed area where a showing class takes place, either 'in hand' where the handler leads the pony, or ridden.

Sibling – where children or animals have the same parent or parents.

Sidle – walking in an unsure manner, especially sideways.

Sleek – where the hair (coat) of the pony is smooth and glossy.

Snort – blowing air through the nostrils at speed to make a noise. Often performed by a horse in a state of excitement, uncertainty or stress.

Sole – the undersurface of a pony's foot (hoof).

Spook – to take fright. To be unnerved. To jump or jolt in fright.

Squeeze from the seat – where the rider uses the muscles in their backside to convey a message (an instruction) to the horse, i.e. to go faster or move in a certain direction.

Squeal – a long high-pitched cry or noise made by a horse, particularly a stallion.

Stable – a building or 'room' in a barn which is used to keep a horse or pony in.

Stag – a male deer (red deer on Exmoor) after its fifth year.

Stallion – an uncastrated male horse over four years old. Stallions can breed with mares to produce foals.

Steed – a horse being ridden, or available for riding.

Straw – dried stalks of wheat, oats and barley, used for horse bedding.

Strife – anger, bitter disagreement or conflict.

Stumble – to trip or momentarily lose balance, to almost fall. If a horse stumbles, the rider can be unseated and fall off.

Tack – the equipment used to ride or lead a horse – such as the bridle and saddle.

Tail – the tail of the horse is a mass of long hair at the base of the spine, consisting of the dock (the muscles and skin covering the coccygeal vertebrae) and the skirt of long hairs that fall below the dock. Horses use their tails to convey communication messages, to swish away flies and to protect them from rain and cold.

Tarpaulin – a heavy duty waterproof cloth that is extremely durable. Often brightly coloured. Tarpaulins are used in Agility to increase the confidence of equines to walk over strange surfaces.

Tense – unable to relax because of anxiety or nervousness.

Terrain – the physical features of an area of land.

Thirst quencher – a drink. For horses and ponies that means water.

Trailer – an unpowered vehicle towed by a powered vehicle. For example, a livestock trailer which can carry ponies inside.

Trot – the second pace or gait of the horse, which is faster than a walk, lifting each diagonal pair of legs alternatively.

Trust – having a firm belief in the reliability, behaviour, truth and ability of someone or something.

Tumble – take a sudden fall.

Unyielding – not giving way to pressure, unresponsive.

Venture – undertaking a potentially risky or daring journey or course of action.

Vet or Veterinary Surgeon – a person qualified to treat diseased or injured animals ie, a 'doctor' for animals.

Veterinary Book – referring to the information available to a vet for consultation when deciding what is wrong with an animal.

Water Vole – a small, typically burrowing, mouse-like rodent which is 'semiaquatic' meaning it also likes to live in water.

Well-Moving – an equestrian term used to describe a horse or pony which is well conformed (has a correct structure) and moves evenly and correctly in all its paces – walk, trot, canter and gallop.

Whicker – a soft breathy noise made by a horse, a gentle sound, often made when greeting a friend or offering comfort or affection.

Whinny – a high-pitched noise made by a horse or pony – a neigh. Often accompanied by tossing their head.

Whip, crop or Showing Cane – a thin flexible length of leather on a short, stiff handle (or an inflexible cane) which is used to reinforce the hand. Sometimes, the whip can be used too harshly as a tool of punishment on a horse, which is discouraged.

Wither – the ridge between the shoulder blades of a horse, at the base of the neck and mane. Where the hands rest when riding.

Yearn – an intense feeling of longing for someone or something.

Yonder – in the far distance, or 'over there'.